Based on an original idea by Alex A.

First published in French in 2015 by Presses Aventure under the title
Les dossiers secrets de Moignons.

Adventure Press Inc.
55 Jean-Talon Street West
Montreal, Quebec, Canada H2R 2W8
adventurepress.ca

President and CEO: Marc G. Alain
Editor: Marie-Eve Labelle
Archive dossier author: Laurence-Marie Dufault
Comic book author: Alex A.
Illustrator: Alex A.
Editorial reviewers: Catherine LeBlanc-Fredette and Flavie Léger-Roy
Graphics designer: Gabrielle Lecomte
Page layout: Vicky Masse-Chaput
Translator: Rhonda Mullins
Proofreader: Sasha Regehr

Legal deposit – Bibliothèque et Archives nationales du Québec, 2019
Legal deposit – Library and Archives Canada, 2019

ISBN: 978-1-77285-035-2 (PAPERBACK)

ISBN: 978-1-77285-039-0 (PDF)
ISBN: 978-1-77285-040-6 (EPUB)
ISBN: 978-1-77285-041-3 (KINDLE)

Government of Quebec – Tax credit for book publishing and business support
program for books and specialized publishing – SODEC

Funded by the Government of Canada | **Canadä**

Printed in China

THE SECRET FILES OF MR. SHORTHAND

ADVENTURE PRESS

TABLE OF CONTENTS

OBJECTIVE: RESISTANCE
Chapter 1

The Agency is no more. Big Beaver has finally won. Thanks to the Agency's super-advanced technology and an alliance with President Tiberius's army, Big Beaver has taken control of the First Continent, which he has rebaptized Big Beaver Land.

But there is still hope. Martha, WXT, Shorthand, Maple, Billy and Henry are alive and, from their secret hideout, they are fighting to find a way to save what remains of their world. They are called the Resistance. As for Agent Jon, he has kept his spirits up and decided to relearn the job of secret agent. He is now an important member of the Resistance. But... will he ever be the legend he used to be? That remains to be seen...

MARTHA

Mission 1, *The Brain of the Apocalypse*

Location:

Building A, First Continent

A dedicated director

In Building A, Martha leads agents in their missions and provides protection for her territory, the First Continent. Serious, professional and above all dedicated, she considers herself a planetary protector. Martha has been wary of Jon since he first became an agent. But so far, he has done nothing to prove her doubts right. That may be why she doesn't laugh at Jon's jokes (okay, his humour can be a little...off)!

OOOOOOOOOO OOOOOOOOOOOO OOOOOOOOOH!

YOU'RE LAYING IT ON PRETTY THICK THERE.

SORRY...

Martha has proven her value time and time again. She is the best Director Building A could ask for!

LATEST UPDATE:

Unfortunately, the conspiracy she had a feeling about turned out to be real! Her doubts were confirmed a while ago when Big Beaver revealed his diabolical plan. Martha did more than just show foresight. Feeling a threat closing in, she developed an emergency plan and built a shelter so we could continue our operations. What instinct. – Maple

First appearance:

Mission 1, *The Brain of the Apocalypse*

Location:

Building A, First Continent

From petty thief to crack agent

Orphaned when he was little, WXT grew up on the streets. He regularly committed petty thefts, until one day he tried to steal a lady's handbag... and that lady was none other than Martha! Furious, but impressed by the young boy's agility and daring, Martha decided to take WXT under her wing.

Lofty ambitions

He soon discovered how impressive the Agency is and, driven by the legends of his hero, Agent S, WXT put his talents to work. His goal is clear: to become the best agent the Agency has ever seen.

The hero

WXT has an unblemished record at the Agency, and he is very proud of that. However, his ambitions are thwarted when a gifted agent appears: Jon Le Bon. For WXT, who is still seeking admiration, this newcomer steals the spotlight on missions where WXT should have been the hero. This rivalry even prompts WXT to leave the Agency...what a loss.

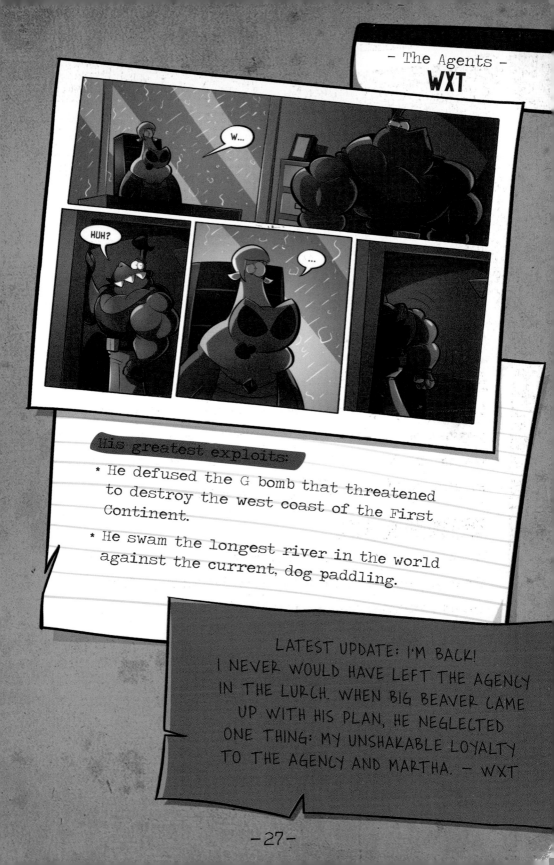

His greatest exploits:

* He defused the G bomb that threatened to destroy the west coast of the First Continent.

* He swam the longest river in the world against the current, dog paddling.

LATEST UPDATE: I'M BACK! I NEVER WOULD HAVE LEFT THE AGENCY IN THE LURCH. WHEN BIG BEAVER CAME UP WITH HIS PLAN, HE NEGLECTED ONE THING: MY UNSHAKABLE LOYALTY TO THE AGENCY AND MARTHA. — WXT

IS THERE SOMETHING ON MY HEAD?

AL

First appearance:

Mission 1, *The Brain of the Apocalypse*

Location:

The beaches of Central Island,
First Continent

Putting his heart into his work

Before his well-earned (but definitely not early) retirement, Al was the oldest

member of the Agency. He created artificial organs which have allowed him

to live for over ~~145~~ 150 years so far! He has a metal heart, foam kidneys and

a woolen pancreas, which he knit with his own hands.

The big leap

Al is now an extreme parachuting instructor on the First Continent's

Central Island, and he is trying to break the record for the highest jump.

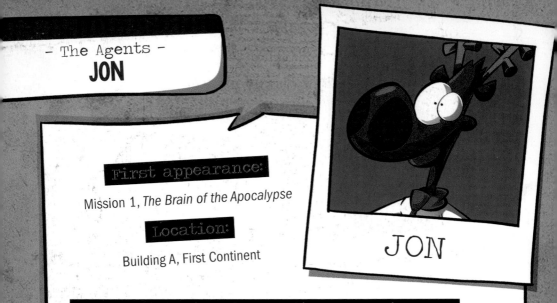

First appearance:

Mission 1, *The Brain of the Apocalypse*

Location:

Building A, First Continent

JON

Saving the world is child's (or fawn's) play

Since joining the Agency, Jon Le Bon has obliterated training test records and saved the world dozens of times. But deep down, he's just a big kid. He is always in a good mood, even when thing seem hopeless; he sees the fun in life and in his job. He is patient and friendly with everyone...even criminals.

Like father, like son

To succeed in his missions, this boisterous secret agent draws inspiration from his heroes: video game and action movie characters...which explains his love of explosions. But even though no one can predict the turns his missions will take, everyone knows that he gets his outstanding qualities as an agent from his father, the legendary Agent S.

Um, actually, these qualities were programmed in me. I mean implanted. Biologically. Or I should say, genetically. Or maybe bio-technical-genetic-whatchamacallit... Argh! Ask Henry to explain it to you! – Jon

Jon's arrival at the Agency when he was just a little baby.

An adorable little Jon playing with his favourite toy gun!

Me and Jon.

Argh! He's so hard to frame!

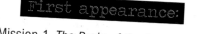

BILLY

First appearance:

Mission 1, *The Brain of the Apocalypse*

Location:

Building A, First Continent

A comical genius

Security manager, computer expert, video game champ: Billy is resourceful and versatile. But despite an impressive IQ of 184, he prefers joking to working, which is why he gets along so well with Agent Jon. Billy clearly isn't the most muscular agent at the Agency (he's even a little wimpy), but it's hard to run on a treadmill when you're a worm!

Hidden vice

Billy is crazy about sugar. He even has a slush machine stashed in his bedroom...which explains his trouble sleeping. He never sleeps more than two hours a day, and he can work up to 144 hours straight!

Cheers to the newlyweds!

Billy and Polo got married! The entire Agency wishes them a great deal of happiness! (Note to self: consider getting rid of the traditional Mr. Shorthand throw.)

LATEST UPDATE:
Polo disappeared in the explosion and Billy is devastated... Has Big Beaver taken everything from us?
– MAPLE

THIS IS THE STRANGEST PLACE I'VE EVER BEEN!

I'M GOING TO TRY TO FIGURE OUT HOW IT WORKS...

HAAA!

WHOA! THE WALL IS ALL WEIRD!

OKAY, DON'T TOUCH ANYTHING ELSE WITHOUT ASKING ME...

STATS AND RECORDS:
* Neutralized 55,000 computer viruses.
* Is fluent in 300 programming languages.
* Crushed close to one million mushrooms in video games.

GERALD

First appearance:

Mission 2, *Formula V*

Location:

Building F, Land of Yellow

Exploits too numerous to tell

Childhood friends, Gerald and Theodore (Agent S) had many adventures together. Their most amazing feat? At age 12, they created a homework shredding robot. That provoked angry reactions from their teachers, but it ended up earning them first prize in the science fair.

Overcome with grief

The two associates and their sidekick, Conrad, were an explosive trio at the Agency...until Theodore disappeared. Gerald will never be the same. Today he is the Building Director in the Land of Yellow, overseeing a continent where criminals run wild.

Air cowboy

There is nothing this daredevil likes more than being at the controls of an aircraft he invented, doing a triple axel followed by a spiral dive!

GET READY TO FLY LIKE YOU'VE NEVER FLOWN BEFORE!

A big softie, Conrad has mastered the art of baking cookies which are a real treat to his beloved son, Creamy Bear...

- The Agents -
CONRAD, ALIAS THE ATOMIC MONKEY

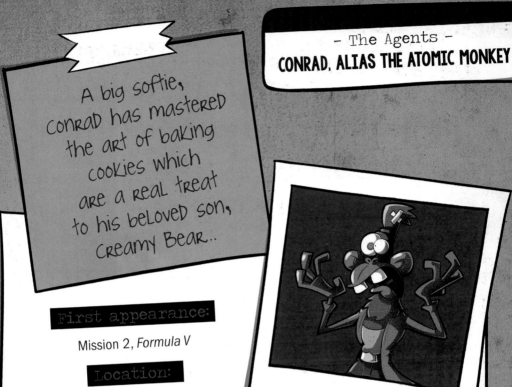

CONRAD

First appearance:

Mission 2, *Formula V*

Location:

Basement of Building K, Antarctica

An explosive team

From a young age, Conrad was a crew member of the *Golden Horse,* the flagship of the First Continent army. He had a number of duties: navigator, science officer, flight physician, and more. Years after the departure of his captain, the legendary Agent S, Conrad, contaminated by Formula V, suffered an irreversible mutation that altered his cognitive functions, forcing him to spend his days in the basement of Building K, with other agents too battered to return to the field.

A unique family

Conrad has a son, Creamy Bear. We don't know why his progeny is a bear and not a monkey or how he gave birth to him himself...and, frankly, we don't want to know.

DR. JULIUS

First appearance:

Mission 3, *Operation Shorthand*

Location:

The ocean floor, on the perimeter of the ruins of Building C

A psychology shark

Dr. Julius has a formidable weapon: psychology. A talented psychiatrist, he specializes in rehabilitating unhinged, dangerous criminals.

In good and many hands

Dr. Julius now lives happily with his wife, a giant, destructive octopus who became a florist after he treated her...

NOTABLE CASES

Borius Reginolf: Julius's first patient was a bloodthirsty mercenary who had lost touch with reality. He was cured at a very advanced age, even though most had lost hope. Today Borius is over 100 years old and lives a quiet life, devoting himself to macramé.

Frank the Rabbit:

A psychopathic murderer.

Previously incapable of feeling emotion, Frank made great strides, but unfortunately he escaped before he could be completely cured.

Whitewash:

An obsessive biologist. Ten years of therapy enabled him to give up his obsessions and stop playing God. Unfortunately, he relapsed, for reasons unknown.

HYLDA

First appearance:

Mission 3, *Operation Shorthand*

Location:

Building C, Pacific Ocean

Ever higher!

Aqua Ma... Hylda is the athlete of the Sisterhood. She excels at everything: martial arts, the outdoors, curling and more. At age 22, she became the first person to climb the Delenor Cliff to the stratosphere, while holding her breath and carrying an anvil in her backpack.

A career making waves

Shortly after becoming an agent, Hylda contracted a virulent bone disease in the Redlands. She barely survived, and her bones are still fragile, which meant ending her activities in the field. But this sort of agent can't be idle for long: Hylda became the head of Building C, making her Martha's aquatic counterpart.

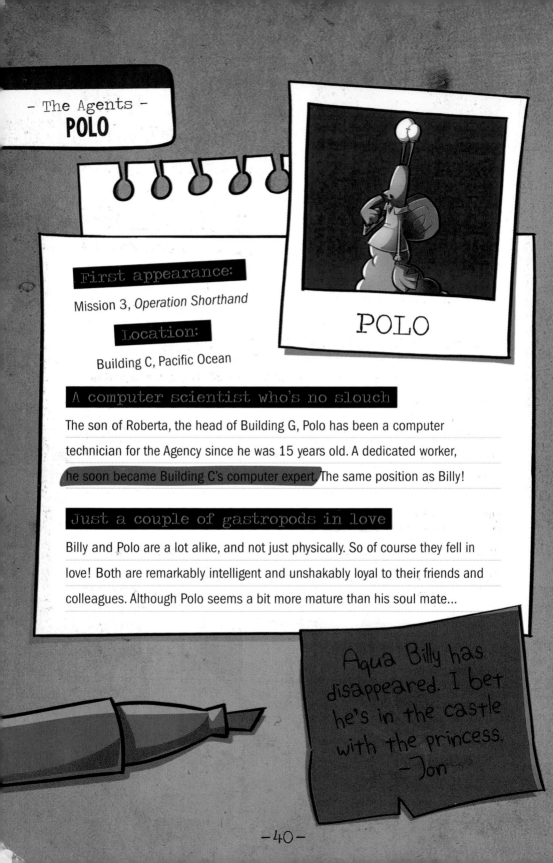

POLO

First appearance:

Mission 3, *Operation Shorthand*

Location:

Building C, Pacific Ocean

A computer scientist who's no slouch

The son of Roberta, the head of Building G, Polo has been a computer technician for the Agency since he was 15 years old. A dedicated worker, he soon became Building C's computer expert. The same position as Billy!

Just a couple of gastropods in love

Billy and Polo are a lot alike, and not just physically. So of course they fell in love! Both are remarkably intelligent and unshakably loyal to their friends and colleagues. Although Polo seems a bit more mature than his soul mate...

Aqua Billy has disappeared. I bet he's in the castle with the princess.
—Jon

FLOPPY

First appearance:

Mission 3, *Operation Shorthand*

Location:

Building K, Antarctica

Pirate, bandit...and cute as all get-out

Floppy (he's so cute!), a former member of the gang of villains in the Land of Yellow, has pirated the surveillance systems of the government and the Agency, leaving his partners in crime to loot the ruins. The gang was eventually caught, and the Agency, impressed by the adorable Floppy's talent, released him in exchange for his services.

A crack computer expert

Floppy is now the computer expert for Building K, the technological heart of the Agency, where he enjoys working on futuristic technologies.

THEODORE

Alias Agent S

First appearance:

Mission 4, *The Prophecy of Four*

Location:

Building A, First Continent

A renaissance agent

Before his military career, Theodore had a number of exciting occupations, including firefighter, race car driver, kindergarten teacher and more. It would be easier to list the things he hasn't done: astronaut... Um, no, I see here he was an astronaut, although briefly. What a guy! But the Agency was where this hero reached his true potential. Thanks to the Agency, he became a legendary secret agent, admired by one and all.

Inseparable enemies

As an agent, Theodore has taken on Big Beaver more than once. His most memorable battle was when the formidable bad guy plotted to make the sun explode, something that Agent S, of course, managed to prevent at the eleventh hour. Long thought dead after a clash with Big Beaver, Theodore recently re-emerged. This incredible agent and his son, Jon, have been reunited.

Um, actually, it's not as simple as that...

NOAH

First appearance:

Mission 4, *The Prophecy of Four*

Location:

It depends

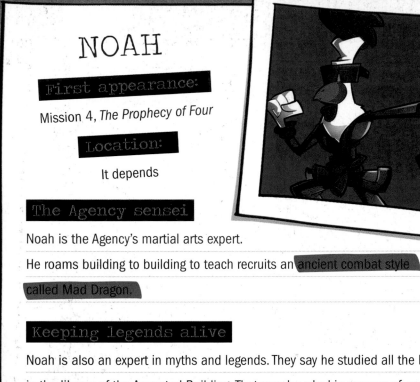

The Agency sensei

Noah is the Agency's martial arts expert.
He roams building to building to teach recruits an ancient combat style called Mad Dragon.

Keeping legends alive

Noah is also an expert in myths and legends. They say he studied all the books in the library of the Ancestral Building. That may be why his manner of speaking is so poetic and obscure...

Favourite pastime

Emerging from shadowy corners to share his mystical knowledge. It helps him cultivate an air of enigma...and impress the girls.

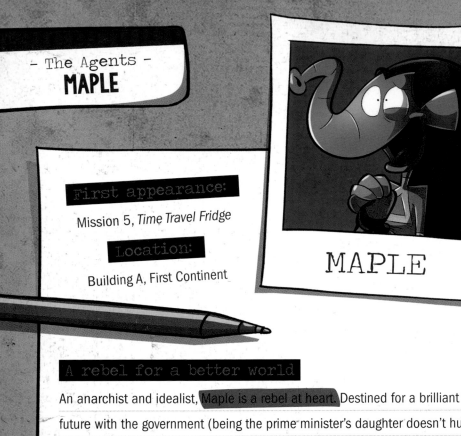

MAPLE

First appearance:

Mission 5, *Time Travel Fridge*

Location:

Building A, First Continent

A rebel for a better world

An anarchist and idealist, Maple is a rebel at heart. Destined for a brilliant future with the government (being the prime minister's daughter doesn't hurt...), she became disillusioned about her employer's fairness and integrity. Even though work is what she cares most about, she would defy authority if she received an order that contradicted her values.

(TRUNK, elephant... Doh! If only someone could read my inventive wordplay!)

A few tricks up her trunk ←

For Maple, joining the Agency was a dream come true, as was being surrounded by fellow non-conformists! An expert spy and infiltrator, Maple uncovered information and technology from the government's Secret Service. She is a perfectionist and a master of cunning and disguise, but what she can't hide is her crush on Jon. She's also pretty bad at insults.

It seems that Maple asked Martha to give her private spy classes... Is she shooting for a directorship?

EVA IS NOT
JUST OUR NURSE!
SHE IS ALSO OUR MECHANIC,
GUNSMITH AND
GENERAL HANDYPERSON.
— WXT

EVA

First appearance:

Mission 7, *The Ultimate Symbol*

Location:

Building A, First Continent

An android with attitude

A wonder of artificial intelligence, EVA was designed by Henry to be his medical assistant (her lack of interest and empathy made some of her diagnoses...surprising). Normally you know what to expect from a computer, but EVA is anything but predictable. With her caustic humour and adventurous spirit, she even manages to surprise her creator. She loves playing tricks and defying authority, and what can you say about her personality... She is so highly developed that she has become a person in her own right.

Holographically yours

After her robotic body was destroyed, EVA transferred her consciousness to a new holographic body, made of light and force fields.

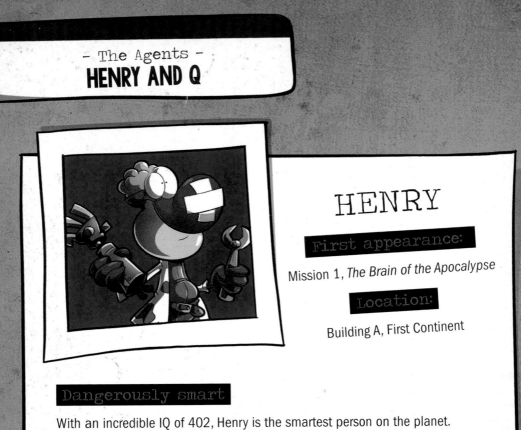

HENRY

First appearance:

Mission 1, *The Brain of the Apocalypse*

Location:

Building A, First Continent

Dangerously smart

With an incredible IQ of 402, Henry is the smartest person on the planet. But beneath his genius exterior hides a timid creature and, astonishingly for a scientist, a superstitious one! What he loves most is discovering parallel worlds, a dangerous occupation, but not as dangerous as discovering his brain has its own consciousness...

Q

First appearance:

Mission 1, *The Brain of the Apocalypse*

Location:

Building A, First Continent

A duelling duo

While Henry is an incredible genius, his brain, Q, is a psychopath... Of course, the brain's diabolical impulses have driven the timid, peace-loving Henry to create destructive inventions, but without Q, would he be as gifted as he is today?

The autonomous brain

Q wasn't made to be held prisoner in a skull! When Whitewash opened Henry's skull, Q seized the opportunity to escape and terrorize the planet (a rare opportunity most psychopathic brains only dream about). Good thing he can be controlled by daily sedative injections...

We recently learned that the anesthetic was made of sugar water and that Q had taken everyone for a ride. Now he is living out his life as an arch-villain with Big Beaver. - Jon

LATEST UPDATE: NOW PARALYZED AND EQUIPPED WITH AN ARTIFICIAL BRAIN INSPIRED BY GABRIEL LOBE'S LUBOLO, HENRY DEVOTES HIS INTELLIGENCE TO IMPROVING HUMANITY. DESPITE IT ALL, HE OFTEN WORRIES ABOUT Q AND IS AFRAID THAT IF HE KEEPS WALKING AROUND NAKED HE WILL CATCH A BRAIN COLD... — WXT

Henry B. Belton's prosthetic brain

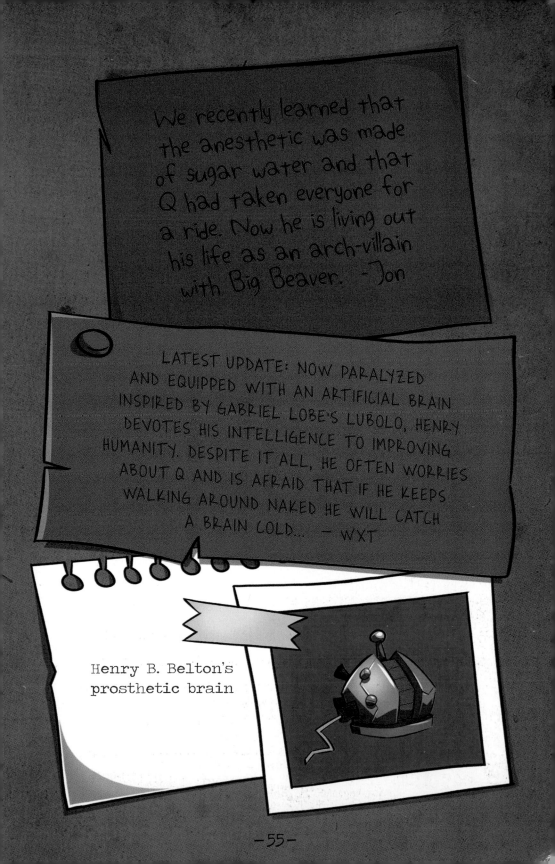

BIG BEAVER HAS TAKEN CONTROL OF THE AGENCY! FOR THE DETAILS OF HIS DIABOLICAL PLAN, SEE FILE NUMBER 138-141.
— WXT

BIG BEAVER

First appearance:

Mission 1, *The Brain of the Apocalypse*

Location:

Unknown

↑

The WORST thing about this arch-villain is his sinister grin...

Sinking his teeth into the Agency

The Agency's ultimate enemy, Big Beaver likes to watch people suffer and loves tackling the impossible.  that makes him a formidable creature, one that can patiently and meticulously develop the most diabolical of plans. He is the most unpredictable criminal the Agency has ever taken on.

Genetic oddity

There are so many mysteries surrounding Big Beaver! Not enough is known about this legendary adversary, and what is known is troubling: he has unparalleled strength and stamina, and twisted intelligence that is thus far unmatched. Even his genes seem more evolved and complex than those of other living creatures. What makes them special? Our leading scientists have no idea...

How old is Big Beaver?

Who would think that such a simple question could cause so much debate among experts! He has been putting a spanner in the Agency's works for so long that he must be over 60 years old. Some people say he is 100 years old, which is hard to believe given how spry and in good physical shape he is. Others go so far as to say that he is as old as the Agency, if not older! But that's just ridiculous. This is real life, not the comics.

WHY ARE YOU STILL SMILING? THIS TIME YOU LOST.

I'M LAUGHING BECAUSE...

...YOU'VE BEEN HAD!

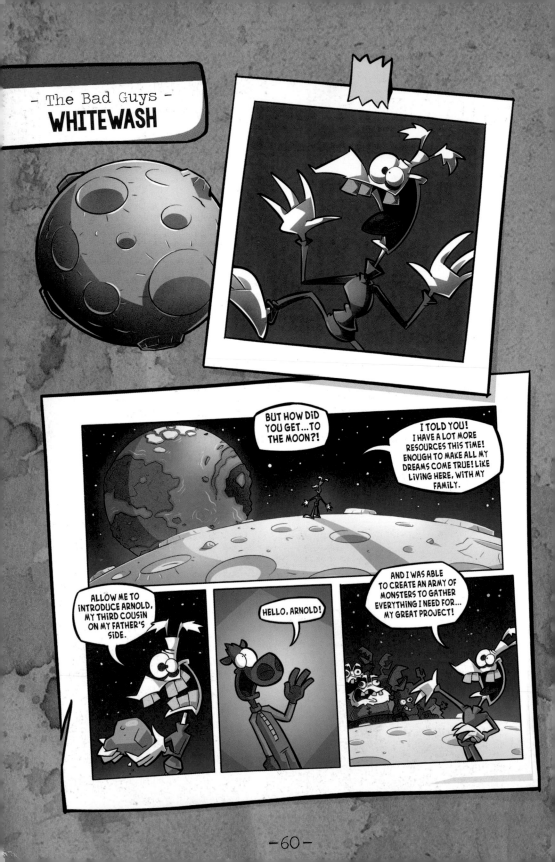

WHITEWASH

First appearance:

Mission 1, *The Brain of the Apocalypse*

Location:

It depends

A modern-day Frankenstein

He is the friendliest of the bad guys, but also the most unstable! Whitewash is a certifiably mad biologist who is obsessed with creating the ultimate being from the body parts of exceptional people. He clumsily tries to become a better evil-doer, but he doesn't have what it takes to be a good bad guy!

A chip off the old rock

When he isn't locked up in his cell or on the run across the continents, Whitewash likes working on the moon. That's where he feels at home, surrounded by his family and friends. Whitewash is a poor orphan who grew up around rocks. It's no wonder he turned out so odd!

So who is Whitewash?!

Whitewash doesn't know who his biological parents are, where he comes from or even what sort of animal he is. Perhaps an anteater? Or a rabbit? You have to admit, he is like nothing we have ever seen.

Ha ha! I know what he is!
— Jon

A young Whitewash

Mozart Lobe's
ball of wool

GABRIEL LOBE

First appearance:

Mission 1, *The Brain of the Apocalypse*

Location:

Building A, First Continent,
in Jon's head

The orange sheep of the family

It's a little-known fact that Gabriel Lobe has an orange woolen twin, Mozart, who died tragically at age 12, just a few days after the annual shearing. The two brothers were so tight-knit that it's like they shared a single mind. Devastated by his death, Gabriel made himself a wool sweater with Mozart's wool, whom he can't stand to be apart from, even today.

Shepherd of a single consciousness

Gabriel Lobe became obsessed with wanting everyone to know the symbiosis he shares with his brother. In an effort to unite the world into a single consciousness, he designed the Intra-neuronal 3000 — or Lobulo — an invention to infiltrate people's minds. It's one seriously dangerous creation! He almost reached his goal.

Neuron prison

Gabriel sacrificed his physical body to become a virtual mind, trapped in the head of Agent Jon! With that sort of intellect, surely he will make it out!

GABRIEL LOBE

AFTER RECEIVING HIS FIRST DICE AT AGE 7, HE DEVELOPED AN ALL-CONSUMING PASSION FOR NUMBERS.

AGE 41, CONSIDERED ONE OF THE GREATEST COMPUTER VIRTUOSOS.

HIS INTEREST IN BINARY PROGRAMMING SOON FOLLOWED.

AS EARLY AS AGE 12, HE COULD DO VIRTUALLY ANYTHING WITH ZEROS AND ONES.

AT AGE 15, HE BUILT HIS FIRST COMPUTER, THE TANGERINE 1.0. THE COMPUTER WAS A BIG HIT!

THANKS TO ITS 2 BITS OF PROCESSING POWER, HE COULD ADD UP NUMBERS AS HIGH AS 13 AND 28! (WITH A 49% MARGIN OF ERROR, A MIRACLE AT THE TIME).

AT AGE 33, GABRIEL CREATED THE TANGERINE 64, THE FIRST ULTRA-PORTABLE COMPUTER.

IN JUST A FEW MONTHS, VIRTUALLY EVERYONE ON EARTH HAD ONE.

GABRIEL HAD ALMOST ACHIEVED HIS MAIN GOAL: CONNECTING EVERY LIVING BEING ON THE PLANET... TO FORM JUST ONE CONSCIOUSNESS.

TIBERIUS

First appearance:

Mission 2, *Formula V*

Location:

Minister's Mansion, First Continent

A crooked crook

Mayor of his small town and then head of the army, Tiberius rose through the ranks to become president of the First Continent. A corrupt politician and power-monger, he is not afraid to use violence. And since he is the most powerful man in mainstream society, he is a bad guy who should never be underestimated.

Public enemy

Tiberius is a sworn enemy of the Agency, which he considers a public danger, but which also makes him green with envy: it's the only organization that is more powerful than his government. His worst enemy is Agent S, who disobeyed him when he was in the army. Tiberius's outsized ego cannot accept being contradicted, even when he is wrong!

Strict father, rebellious daughter

Tiberius has one daughter, Maple, who rebelled against him and joined the ranks of the Agency. He's furious that she has defied his authority, but he still loves her...

The Formula V episode wasn't Creamy Bear's first attempt at world domination. He had already transformed his teddy bears into vicious cyborgs using technology developed by his father…

CREAMY BEAR

First appearance:

Mission 2, *Formula V*

Location:

Basement of Building K, Antarctica

Playing with fire

Creamy Bear is a little boy (well, not so little) trapped in his own world who has a hard time telling fact from fiction. He sees the planet as a giant playground. Some kids play dolly; Creamy Bear plays great scientist destroying the planet. But when you are the son of Conrad the Atomic Monkey and you can get your hands on toys like Formula V, safety goes out the window!

Mutants, father and son

After his crushing failure with Formula V, Creamy Bear suffered a serious mutation that had irreversible effects on his brain and made him barking mad. He is now locked up with his father — who has also become a mutant — in the basement of Building K. How sad!

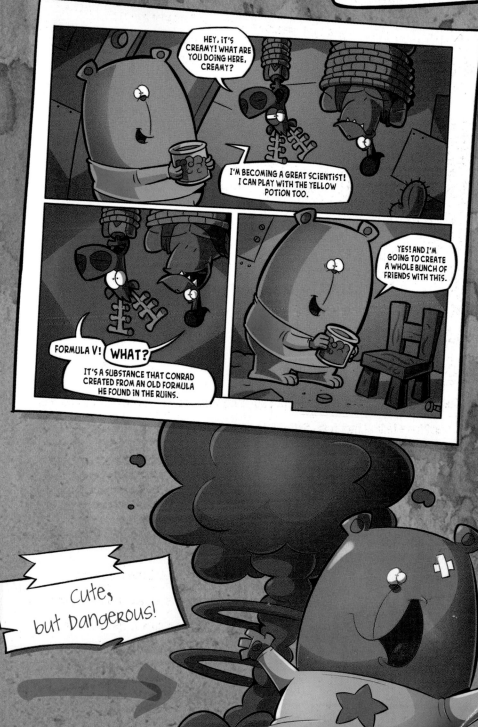

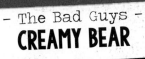

First appearance:

Mission 4, *The Prophecy of Four*

Location:

Building F, Land of Yellow

Young and rebellious

Cassandra, Martha and Hylda met at school. The three teens, who soon became inseparable, had a lot in common: disdain for authority, a rebellious spirit... But Cassandra stood out: always a crazy scheme, an idea taken too far... In the hallways, people would whisper as she walked by: "Have you heard? She ran away from home at age 13, and I hear she lives alone in the big city..."

Girl gang

When Martha, Hylda and Cassandra grew up they formed a militant group, the Sisterhood, which was soon recruited by the Agency. Martha quickly climbed the ranks, followed closely by Hylda. Cassandra was jealous and had a hard time competing, but ended up achieving agent status as well.

Consumed by jealousy

Shortly after joining the Agency, Cassandra was approached by its sworn enemy, Big Beaver. He had no trouble convincing her that her friends had always humiliated her and that she must seek revenge. She secretly worked for him until she became the head of Building Z, ironically thanks to Martha's unflagging support, and that's when she revealed her true colours...

Oh ya? What colour was she before? – Jon

THE SISTERHOOD.

UM... WHAT'S UP WITH THE NAME?

I KNOW. I KNOW... WE WERE YOUNG.

ARCHIVES 44

SO, JON IS IN GOOD HANDS?

GANG OF VILLAINS

Years later, Cassandra founded her own terrorist cell, the Club of Rebels, with her son Fury and the octogenarian Hostilia. They may seem a bit ridiculous, but it's best to keep an eye on them!

AND THIS IS **FURY**, MY SON.

PLEASURE! **ARGHEU!!!** IS HE ALRIGHT?

OH, DON'T WORRY ABOUT HIM. HIS OXYGEN SUPPLY WAS CUT OFF A LITTLE WHEN HE WAS BORN.

First appearance:

Mission 1, *The Brain of the Apocalypse*

Location:

Building F, Land of Yellow

FURY

Fire and fury

To reward Cassandra for her loyalty, Big Beaver gives her an incredible gift: a son identical to Fury, the mythical horse of the god Colbert! Well, almost identical... The genetic creation has the desired mythological physique, but his intellect leaves — not to put too fine a point on it — a little to be desired. He has never been able to speak, but he understands language. Despite it all, nothing can alter Cassandra's love for him, because she sees him as a divine son, destined for greatness!

Dragon breath

When he was young, he ate a huge pile of hot chilies, thinking they were jujubes, which is why he can now breathe fire.

HOSTILIA

First appearance:

Mission 4, *The Prophecy of Four*

Location:

Secret lab, The Redlands

Ruling the world, one banana at a time

Why rule the world? It would make things so much simpler...and it's something to do! At least that's what the jaded old Hostilia thinks; the geneticist even went so far as to clone an army of bananas to do her laundry and, in their spare time, invade the Earth.

Genetic genius

Hostilia worked with Neziel, the head of Building S, to stabilize the ecosystem by balancing the wildlife population. But she didn't exactly use genetics for good... She had some fun creating super-powerful and aggressive clones. She couldn't resist: she loves monsters and mutants. That was when she met Cassandra, with whom she later founded the Club of Rebels.

LATEST UPDATE:
Hostilia's expertise in experimental genetics helped Big Beaver create the perfect clone from the DNA of Agent S. — Maple

BLOODTHIRSTY BANANAS

First appearance:

Mission 4, *The Prophecy of Four*

Location:

The Redlands

Barbarity and bananary

The Bloodthirsty Bananas are a savage gang that is particularly aggressive and high in potassium. People are afraid they will leave their peels lying around. Clearly that would be dangerous.

Alan the Banana

Hostilia didn't use just anyone's DNA to create her army; she opted for the most inhuman fruit there is: Alan the Banana, the legendary creature of the Redlands. There is no shortage of terrifying words to describe him: a barbarian, a brute, a bandit, a bully, a beast and... a bruised banana.

LATEST UPDATE: ULTRA JON HAS CHANGED SINCE HENRY AND Q LOCKED HIM AWAY IN THE PURPLE DIMENSION. TIME GOES BY MUCH FASTER THERE, SO NOW HE HAS THE WISDOM OF THE AGES... — WXT

ULTRA JON

First appearance:

Mission 1, *The Brain of the Apocalypse*

Location:

The Purple Dimension

Clone from another universe

When Jon touched the Phobos Cube, his DNA was recorded in the memory of the concentrate of purple matter, creating Ultra Jon, a demonic, ultra-powerful version of Agent Jon. Ultra Jon is convinced of his superiority among all beings.

Ultra-powerful

way cool!

Able to steal and shoot lasers with his eyes, Ultra Jon's physical strength is one thousand times greater than that of Agent Jon. And as if that weren't enough, he is immortal, speaks every language in the universe and can even move through matter!

Deep down, he's not so bad. He's just a little guy who wants to find his parents...
—Jon

THE YELLOW ENTITY

First appearance:

Mission 5, *Time Travel Fridge*

Location:

Building A, Henry's lab

Child of light

Made of pure liquid light, the Yellow Entity is a child from a parallel dimension who wants to go back to his world.

When a consciousness is associated with yellow light, its will and emotions control the surrounding space-time. This is why time stops around the Yellow Entity when he is afraid.

JON FROM THE YEAR EIGHT MILLION

First appearance:

Mission 5, *Time Travel Fridge*

Location:

Pops up here and there
in the space-time fabric

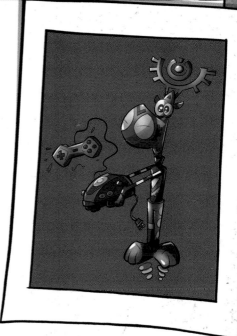

On the road of time

In eight million years (give or take), thanks to purple energy, a derivative of purple matter, all living beings will be able to travel the timeline as if on a road. However, these new creatures will have travelled so much that their own era will have been lost, forever abandoned. As a result, many travellers will be trapped in time, belonging to no era; they will be called the Paradoxals. Astonishingly, Jon is now one of them. He seems to have survived so far...

Wow! Am I ever old!
But come to think of it...
How do you know this,
Shorthand? –Jon

THE BEHEPAS

THE BEHEPAS

First appearance:

Mission 2, *Formula V*

Location:

Land of Yellow

Ancient and mysterious

The peaceful civilization of the Behepas, now extinct, dates back 12,000 years. The Behepas developed highly advanced technology, about which little is understood...because almost no one can decipher their language! They are in fact — and this information is TOP SECRET — aliens from Venus that worship the goddess of light, Luceta.

Living knowledge

This ancient peoples erected many mysterious constructions, including the high tower that features the equation of a primordial force called...life. Thanks to this people, Conrad created Formula V. And thanks to it the Guardians of Life — Octavias, Onizine, Ovidor and Billy Bob — come back to life and lend Agent Jon a hand.

Horus

THE NEO-MARTIANS

First Appearance:

Mission 4, *The Prophecy of Four*

Location:

The Redlands

Grotesque good guys

Despite its cruel look, this people is actually one of the most civilized in the Redlands: its members refuse to kill or torture other creatures. They are even vegetarians!

Rhythm and ritual

Their motto is *Daucus Carota*, which they chant during sacred ceremonies. What does that mean? They don't know themselves...but it sounds cool, don't you think?

Mutant divinity

Their god Horus is an ordinary Neo-Martian who became a mutant after being bitten by a radioactive horsefly (it happens more often than you would think!). Despite his impressive strength and size, if you stroke Horus with the nap of his fur, he is pretty gentle.

THE SECT OF SPECTRES

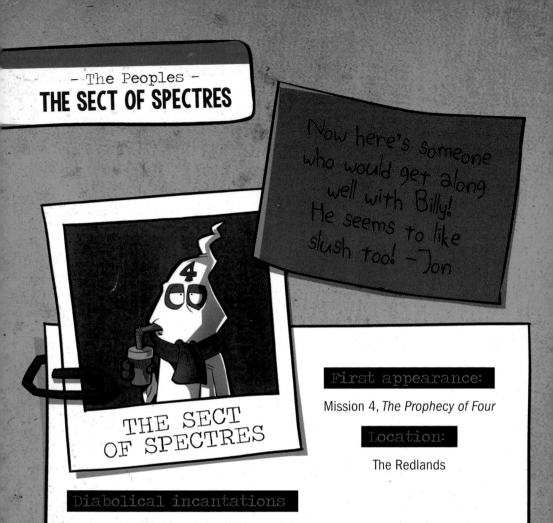

Now here's someone who would get along well with Billy! He seems to like slush too! –Jon

THE SECT OF SPECTRES

First appearance:

Mission 4, *The Prophecy of Four*

Location:

The Redlands

Diabolical incantations

A Redlands cult with a name that is hard to say, the Sect of Srepters...the Sector of Spectors...no, that's not it...the Sect of Spectacles! Argh! The thingamajig's (!) mission is to guard and protect the book of *The Prophecy of Four*, which is intended to bring the terrible demon Kastaro back to life. Thanks to him, the cult members will finally dominate the world (which is all the rage these days!).

Not easy to beat

The Great Wobash, the last living dinosaur, protects the members of the sect. In exchange, the sect members grow flowers that spit fire and mushrooms that make him grow.

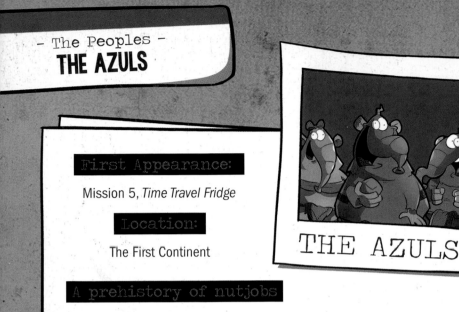

THE AZULS

First Appearance:

Mission 5, *Time Travel Fridge*

Location:

The First Continent

A prehistory of nutjobs

This primitive tribe is made up of elephants, tusked creatures who like nothing more than to wallow in mud. It doesn't take much to surprise them: anything they are unfamiliar with is the work of a god or a demon... You have to give them a break; they lived 200,000 years ago. At the time, the Internet didn't exist, and elephants weren't very educated.

A big illusion

To leave traces of their "greatness," the Azuls build majestic cities, impenetrable fortresses and mysterious pyramids...that were already in ruins. Seriously!
That way, they would be admired in the future for their architectural prowess, without requiring the knowledge such a quality demands in the present.
In reality, they don't need anything other than their mud huts to be happy.

What's there to do in the Stone Age?

Their favourite pastimes are making fire, inventing the wheel, dying at age twenty-eight, waging war with their neighbours the Amarillos, and, most of all, going skinny dipping.

THE FLUIDMORPH CRYOPLASMICS

First appearance:

Mission 5, *Time Travel Fridge*

Location:

It changes, but mainly in Antarctica

ARCHIMEDES PLASMA

Radical transformations

The Fluidmorph Cryoplasmics have the same physical properties as water: at room temperature, they are liquid and get around in small puddles, and they float in clouds in extreme heat. No wonder they prefer glacial climates, where they become solid and can move normally.

Endangered

Curious and peace-loving, the Fluidmorph Cryoplasmics seek out adventure, a character trait that makes them excellent agents. Unfortunately, they have only a few representatives left. To protect them, the Agency is studying them and has a number of them within its ranks, including Archimedes Plasma, the head of Building K.

UM... DO YOU THINK
IT'S NORMAL THAT AN ICE
CUBE HOPS TO GET AROUND?
— WXT

PURPLE MATTER

First appearance:

Mission 1, *The Brain of the Apocalypse*

A matter to think about

A substance with mysterious properties considered the antithetical element to liquid light, purple matter seemed to have purely destructive properties. Legend has it that a special being brought some back from a trip to a parallel dimension thousands of years ago. However, in addition to supplying all the energy required for Building A, it was discovered that the Agency's purple matter cube can also store data. Any direct contact is stored in its memory, and the cube can create the clones of anyone who has touched it. This was how Ultra Jon was born.

Jon DiDn't explode when he touched the Purple matter cube... why not?

PURPLE DIMENSION

When sufficiently concentrated, purple matter offers access to a parallel universe, called the Purple Dimension. They say it is peopled by super-powerful mutants, who are generally purple.

There is no logical explanation. Only a superior being could answer the question...
—Maple

THE GOLDEN HORSE

First appearance:

Mission 2, *Formula V*

Location:

The wreckage is spread across the Land of Yellow

A dream crew

A high-tech aircraft designed by the army, the *Golden Horse* was the flagship of the First Continent fleet. Conrad the Atomic Monkey, Gerald the Flying Hog and Captain Theodore formed its first and only squad. What a crew!

Treasure found

Around ten years after Jon's birth, Tiberius gave the crew of the *Golden Horse* the mission to bombard an enemy base. To prevent the carnage, Theodore and his crew mutinied and disappeared with the assault aircraft, which was then left to rust...until Creamy Bear stole it, and then destroyed it in his attempt to contaminate Earth with Formula V.

The *Golden Horse* was equipped with cutting-edge technology: a flame thrower, ultrasonic radar, an ice cream maker... it had it all!

IT'S TRUE THAT IT'S HARD TO MAKE PERFECTLY GOLDEN TOAST!
— WXT

First appearance:

Mission 2, *Formula V*

Location:

Building A, First Continent

THE TOASTER OF THE GODS AND THE TIME TRAVEL FRIDGE

The beloved golden toaster

The Behepas initially created the Toaster of the Gods to make perfectly golden toast. But engineers made a decimal point error in their calculations and found out that their invention allowed them to travel through time instead. As gadgets go, it wasn't highly valued at first, and the Toaster of the Gods was long forgotten, until war broke out between the Martians and Venusians, and the fall of those civilizations forced the two clans to settle on Earth. Deprived of the best of their technology, the Venusian survivors fell back on the tatters of their society: a few artifacts, including the Toaster of the Gods, now protected by the Guardians of Life.

Kitchen of the future

Henry developed the Time Travel Fridge
through reverse engineering, i.e.,
by studying how the Toaster of the
Gods worked, then reproducing
it on a larger scale. He adapted
the consumption of fuel, liquid light,
so that a single drop made it possible
to travel thousands of years back
in time. Liquid light is one of the
scarcest substances in the universe.
It mustn't be wasted!

Nothing to worry about

The agents that take the Time Travel Fridge enjoy a deodorized trip thanks
to Henry, who regularly changes the box of baking soda.

The Time Travel Fridge is an experimental
device, so it is still not understood
exactly how it works or why... And it's
pretty strange to see the remains of
pterodactyl toast pop out of it. —Jon

FORMULA V

First appearance:

Mission 2, *Formula V*

Formula that could use reformulation

Obtained by solving the Equation of Life found in the ruins of the ancient civilization of the Behepas, Formula V can give life to inanimate objects. It can also overload a being's life force. But careful! It must be handled with care! It hasn't been perfected and horrible mutations can result (WXT has a pretty good memory of this).

YES, I REMEMBER.
— WXT

Venusian legend

It was on their home planet of Venus that the Behepas received the enigmatic Equation of Life from Luceta, their goddess. She wanted to give her people the life force of the gods so that they could become divine too. Obviously that didn't work out so well.

- The Objects -
LOBULO

Gamma ray antenna
that can penetrate
the mind of any living
being on the planet.

CPU 62094XW3
The fastest
processor
ever designed.

LOBULO

First appearance:

Mission 5, *Time Travel Fridge*

Location:

Building K, Antarctica

An idea in mind

Gabriel Lobe developed Lobulo as a giant, functional, super-smart brain, his ultimate creation, meant to revolutionize computer science! However, Lobe secretly wants to use it to hack into every mind on Earth and impose his consciousness on them all. It's a great way to become the master of the world.

Spare organ

After Gabriel Lobe's ruin, Henry copied the components of the original computer to create a new artificial brain, the Lobulo 2.0.

The Lobulo 2.0 doesn't even have a USB 3.0 connection!
—Jon

It's what fuels the Toaster of the Gods and the Time Travel Fridge!
— Maple

LIQUID LIGHT

First appearance:

Mission 5, *Time Travel Fridge*

Blinding power

From a parallel dimension, liquid light is a photon concentrate in plasmic form. This substance, with its impressive energetic power, seems to be the polar opposite of purple matter. The power of a single drop of liquid light is equal to that of six of our suns! It also makes it possible to reach warp speed (speed of light is for suckers!) and to alter space-time.

Top secret

Liquid light is the missing ingredient in Conrad's Formula V; it's the key element in the elixir of life!

GRAVITON
RESERVOIR
↗

Gravitons = theoretical elementary particles. Existence not yet proven by experiments. WOULD explain gravity at the microscopic level!

First appearance:

Mission 7, *The Ultimate Symbol*

Location:

Under the ruins of Building T, smack in the middle of the ocean

Green energy

This reservoir is a complex machine with a turbine fueled by the gravitational power of artificial particles: gravitons. They are programmed to create variations in gravity, enabling the movement of the spherical reservoir. The result is a clean, infinite source of energy, the power of which can't be beat! So long, hydroelectric dams!

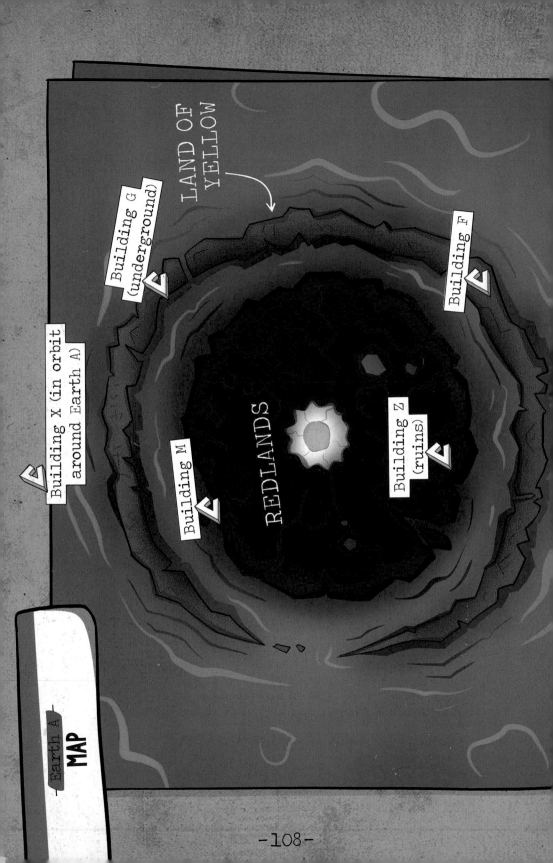

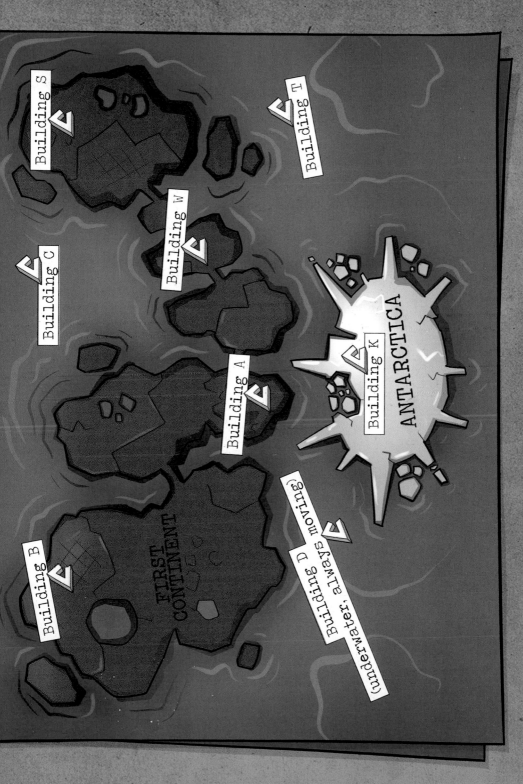

TERRITORIES

The First Continent

The First Continent is where the majority of the population of Earth A lives. Because of its large land mass, the First Continent is also home to the most diverse ecosystem on the planet. The entire region is governed by President Tiberius, in a democratic system, but corrupted by money and organized crime.

The Redlands

A hostile, volcanic continent, the Redlands are home to few species of animals, and the chemical instability of the soil prevents vegetation from taking hold. This country is divided into some thirty tiny governments that, despite their large armies, have little authority over the population. If you're a villain looking for a hideout beyond the long arm of the law, the Redlands is the perfect place for you!

The Land of Yellow

The soil of the Land of Yellow is rich in crystal and precious stone deposits. These lands are also home to the ruins of Behepas temples, a veritable treasure trove. No civilization calls it their home, so the only governments are those of primitive aboriginal tribes.

Antarctica

Ice, ice and more ice, as far as the eye can see... Only a handful of walruses and polar bears inhabit this glacial continent. However, buried kilometres under this immense glacier are archeological treasures that tell the secret story of Earth A, and they still haven't been discovered.

The Monolithic Dimension

This strange dimension appears to Maple and Jon when the presence of the Entity, a being made of pure liquid light, affects the timeline of the universe, which disrupts the flow of things; past, present and future events and characters attract each other and are fused into generalized chaos where everything happens at the same time.

MAJOR BUILDINGS

THE AGENCY'S MAJOR BUILDINGS are at the forefront of the most sophisticated technology. If there is a serious armed conflict, the buildings and their staff will be the front line of defense.

Building A

BACKGROUND: Located on the southern side of the First Continent, Building A was the first building the Agency ever built. It is equipped with the most advanced technologies, giving it symbolic importance and prestige within the Agency. **LED BY:** Martha. (See file 22-25.)

Henry's lab.

Martha's office.

Jon in his bedroom in Building A.

The infirmary.

ARTHUR

Building B

BACKGROUND: Also built on the First Continent, Building B is further north than Building A. **LED BY:** Arthur, the Agency's most senior member. He began his career in the army of the First Continent, where he quickly rose through the ranks and went on to run in national elections against Tiberius. Defeated because of a smear campaign, Arthur decided to approach the Agency, a group of outlaw spies that he discovered while on a mission for the army. He retrained as a field agent and went on to become a building director.

Building C

BACKGROUND: This floating station off the coast of the First Continent is home to a large number of aquatic special agents. It is built on top of the underwater ruins of the previous building, which sank a few years back after an attack by a giant octopus; virtually all the agents who were inside at the time disappeared.

LED BY: Hylda. (See file 38-39.)

DisappeareD... Just Like my PRECiOUS hanDs!

Building F

BACKGROUND: This former military base transformed into an Agency building is located in the heart of the Land of Yellow. Largely underground, Building F specializes in surveillance technology. **LED BY:** Gerald. (See file 34.)

Typical (hostile!) specimen of the Spiteful Penguin that populate the territories surrounding Building K.

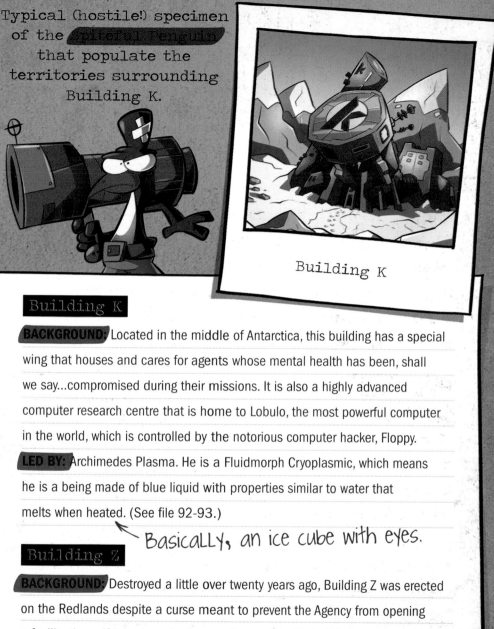

Building K

Building K

BACKGROUND: Located in the middle of Antarctica, this building has a special wing that houses and cares for agents whose mental health has been, shall we say...compromised during their missions. It is also a highly advanced computer research centre that is home to Lobulo, the most powerful computer in the world, which is controlled by the notorious computer hacker, Floppy.

LED BY: Archimedes Plasma. He is a Fluidmorph Cryoplasmic, which means he is a being made of blue liquid with properties similar to water that melts when heated. (See file 92-93.)

← *Basically, an ice cube with eyes.*

Building Z

BACKGROUND: Destroyed a little over twenty years ago, Building Z was erected on the Redlands despite a curse meant to prevent the Agency from opening a facility there. If it had survived more than a day, this building would have been the Agency's largest correctional centre. Its mandate was to rehabilitate (or rather, neutralize) the most hardened criminals on the planet. **LED BY:** Cassandra. She was the only director the building ever had. Unfortunately she betrayed her colleagues and doomed her own building... (See file 70-71.)

MINOR BUILDINGS

THE MINOR BUILDINGS, while less armed and less technological than the major buildings, are essential to the Agency. Their strategic locations allow the Agency to watch over the innermost recesses of the planet.

The Ancestral Building

BACKGROUND: Considered a minor building because it has no tactical role — in addition to being situated in a parallel universe — the Ancestral Building is pretty much a museum and archives for the Agency. **LED BY:** Nobody.

Building D

BACKGROUND: A gigantic tactical submarine, Building D patrols the Southern Ocean, where plenty of arch-villains have sought exile to consider their diabolical plans. **LED BY:** Pearl. An expert archeologist and gifted linguist, she is passionate about studying ancient civilizations buried below the glaciers.

Building G

BACKGROUND: This building is located in an old, abandoned crystal mine of the Land of Yellow so the Agency can keep an eye on any suspicious activity brewing in the continent's basement. **LED BY:** Roberta. A former officer of the First Continent army (like Theodore, Conrad and Gerald), she is also the mother of Polo, Billy's fiancé.

Building M

BACKGROUND: The terrible curse preventing the Agency from operating from the Redlands meant that this building had to be located on a volcanic island off the coast of the continent: the nest of vipers absolutely has to be watched, but from afar! **LED BY:** Myrna. Until recently, she was a 93-year-old woman ravaged by a horrible disease, but her consciousness was transferred to a new body by the building doctor, Octave, who was unwilling to see her die...

Building S

BACKGROUND: This building is nestled within the confines of the tropical forest on the eastern part of the First Continent and specializes in environmental research to protect the ecosystem. Its scientists developed giant filters that eliminate carbon gas, and the building is now used as a global air purifier.
LED BY: Neziel, experimental biochemist and meteorologist.

PEARL   ROBERTA   MYRNA   NEZIEL

Building T

BACKGROUND: This recent construction is in the middle of the ocean. The Agency uses it to study a variety of cutting-edge technologies, including the first graviton reservoir ever built. **LED BY:** Theresa. She was the most recent person admitted to the Council of Twelve, the youngest agent to reach that rank.

Building W

BACKGROUND: This is where, lost somewhere in the swampy expanses in the east of the First Continent, the Agency develops its leading-edge medical care.
LED BY: Ubalda. She is a Mucosiphile, a species of spineless, green beings with the ability to regenerate on their own.

Building X

BACKGROUND: Nestled on a space station in orbit around Earth, from which the Agency can monitor extraterrestrial threats, the entire building is operated by its only director. To accomplish this feat, this odd character connects its mind directly to the building's computer system. This genius apparently has a level-13 intellect. What does that mean? We don't know exactly. All we know is that he is brilliant. He must know what that means! **LED BY:** ????

Who is this guy?
No one ever talks
about him.
—Jon

OBJECTIVE: RESISTANCE
Chapter 2

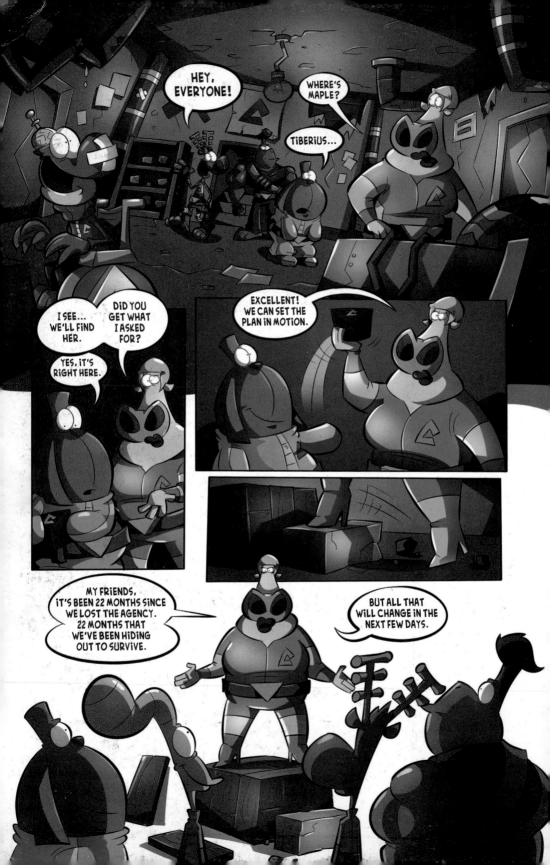

alexbd.com/en/omega-plan

Martha told me your
first name is Emmanuel.
That's a funny name!

MR. SHORTHAND

First appearance:

Mission 1, *The Brain of the Apocalypse*

Location:

Building A, First Continent

A WALKING ENCYCLOPEDIA

Shorthand is the Agency's professor. And not
just that: he also handles communications
and maintains the archives. He knows everything
there is to know about the agents and criminals.
The proof: his secret files!

LOSING HIS HANDS WITHOUT LOSING HIS TOUCH

He used to be a field agent like us, until one
of Whitewash's monsters cut off his hands.
But it doesn't seem to bother him all that
much. He can still write, draw, butter toast
and operate the controls of a helicopter!
How does he do it!?

THAT'S WHAT I'D LIKE
TO KNOW! — WXT

APPENDIX

BIG BEAVER'S PLAN

by Jon, WXT, Maple
and Shorthand!

BIG BEAVER'S PLAN

A BOMBSHELL THAT LEFT US GOBSMACKED: Big Beaver was manipulating the characters and events for his own ends since the beginning! His goal? To gain control of the Agency. To do this, Big Beaver developed an incredibly complex, Machiavellian plan that we understood in part when he revealed to Jon the details of his incredible scheme. But have we cleared up the whole mystery? The two years spent in the bunker helped us understand some of what was hiding in the shadows.

- **A LONG-TERM ALLIANCE WITH Q: HOW IS THAT POSSIBLE?**

Henry never knew it, but he has been living a double life: an honest scientist by day and an arch-villain by night. This explains why terrorist groups have been interested in him and kept kidnapping him. Eventually, Big Beaver noticed the contradictions and understood that Henry B. Belton's brain had its own will, which was active when the host slept. One evening when Henry was sleeping peacefully, Big Beaver met Q and explained his diabolical plan, a plan that of course won over the demented brain, and a new alliance was born.

- **WHY DID BIG BEAVER MANIPULATE CREAMY BEAR TO CREATE AN ARMY OF MUTANTS?** Big Beaver took a real interest in Gerald and Conrad, two former agents, well before Jon met them. He even put them under close surveillance on the abandoned military base where they live. This is how he learned about Conrad's progress with Formula V. Even more worrisome, he understood that he could use it in executing his infamous plan. It was precisely the missing piece that would allow him to create the perfect clone from his DNA and that of Agent S: Jon. Once Jon became an agent, Big Beaver had to create fake enemies for him to defeat so he could gain the Agency's confidence (and particularly that of Martha). So he turned to Conrad's son, Creamy Bear, and convinced him to steal and spread Formula V. Poor Creamy Bear, who just wants to make his father proud of him, doesn't know that Big Beaver planned everything: from his arrest by Agent Jon to his imprisonment below Building K.

- **WHITEWASH, A FORMIDABLE ENEMY...MADE TO MEASURE?** Big Beaver created Whitewash, then secretly watched him his whole life, until he became an adult, when he finally approached him to make him a Machiavellian ally. Whitewash has great potential as an arch-villain...but he doesn't always have the resources he needs for his twisted plans! So Big Beaver is always behind his schemes: he provided him a hideout to kidnap Henry B. Belton and cutting-edge equipment to chop off agents' limbs, and he even saved him after his crushing failure on the Moon thanks to the genetic therapy developed to create his clones.

Big Beaver:
the powerful driving
force behind most
of Whitewash's
misdeeds.

Big Beaver exiting
the Time Travel Fridge.

- **BUT WHERE DOES THE ANCIENT PROPHECY COME FROM THAT FORETOLD THE FOUR ENDS OF THE WORLD?** Still in contact with Q at night, Big Beaver knows that Henry created a prototype of a machine to travel back in time. So he infiltrated the Agency to use it to go back to the era of the Azuls and hand them The Prophecy of Four himself...

- **WHAT IS THE RELATIONSHIP BETWEEN TIBERIUS AND BIG BEAVER?** Big Beaver quickly understood that the president of the First Continent would be an invaluable ally. A criminal, corrupt head of state, Tiberius was easy to convince: Big Beaver used the Time Travel Fridge to show him a terrifying vision of the future where Big Beaver rules the world. Tiberius had no choice but to team up with the arch-villain, preferring to lend him support than potentially be enslaved. Big Beaver also revealed to Tiberius information that Tiberius wanted more than anything: the location of the Agency, a longstanding enemy whom he absolutely wanted to neutralize.

SUPER AGENT JON LE BON: THE ANIMATED MINISERIES ON cbckids.ca

1 — THE BRAIN OF THE APOCALYPSE

2 — FORMULA V

3 — OPERATION SHORTHAND

4 — THE PROPHECY OF FOUR

5 — TIME TRAVEL FRIDGE

6 — A SHEEP IN THE HEAD

7 — THE ULTIMATE SIMBOL

8 — BIG BEAVER FOREVER

THE SECRET FILES OF MR. SHORTHAND